Masterworks for Violin

POÈME
Op. 25
for Violin and Piano
by ERNEST CHAUSSON

Edited by Endre Granat

Piano

KEISER®

PREFACE

Poème for Violin and Piano

When the great Belgian violin virtuoso Eugène Ysaÿe tried to commission a violin concerto, **Ernest Chausson** (1855-1899) declined and suggested a one movement work, *Poème* Op 25. (1896). The premiere took place at the Conservatoire of Nancy in 1896 with Ysaÿe as soloist. The first Paris performance (1897) was a huge success for the composer who was yet relatively unknown. Chausson wrote three versions of the *Poème*: with orchestra, with piano accompaniment, and a version for violin, piano with string quartet, the same setting as his *Concerto in D* for piano, violin and string quartet Op. 21 (1892). The violin parts are identical in all three versions. Ysaÿe's helping hand in writing a most violinistic solo part is noticeable throughout the composition.

Endre Granat, Editor

About the Editor

Endre Granat has studied with Zoltan Kodaly, Gyorgy Ligeti and Jascha Heifetz and is the premier concertmaster for the Hollywood film industry. He has performed with legendary conductors George Szell, Sir Georg Solti and Zubin Mehta. He is a Laureate of the Queen Elizabeth International competition and recipient of the Grand Prix du Disque and the Ysaÿe Medal.

POÈME

Edited by
ENDRE GRANAT

ERNEST CHAUSSON
Op. 25

About the Editor

Endre Granat has studied with Zoltan Kodaly, Gyorgy Ligeti and Jascha Heifetz and is the premier concertmaster for the Hollywood film industry. He has performed with legendary conductors George Szell, Sir Georg Solti and Zubin Mehta. He is a Laureate of the Queen Elizabeth International competition and recipient of the Grand Prix du Disque and the Ysaÿe Medal.

Masterworks for Violin

POÈME
Op. 25
for Violin and Piano
by ERNEST CHAUSSON

Edited by Endre Granat

Violin

KEISER®

PREFACE

Poème for Violin and Piano

When the great Belgian violin virtuoso Eugène Ysaÿe tried to commission a violin concerto, **Ernest Chausson** (1855-1899) declined and suggested a one movement work, *Poème* Op 25. (1896). The premiere took place at the Conservatoire of Nancy in 1896 with Ysaÿe as soloist. The first Paris performance (1897) was a huge success for the composer who was yet relatively unknown. Chausson wrote three versions of the *Poème*: with orchestra, with piano accompaniment, and a version for violin, piano with string quartet, the same setting as his *Concerto in D* for piano, violin and string quartet Op. 21 (1892). The violin parts are identical in all three versions. Ysaÿe's helping hand in writing a most violinistic solo part is noticeable throughout the composition.

Endre Granat, Editor

POÈME

Edited by
ENDRE GRANAT

ERNEST CHAUSSON
Op. 25

Lento e misterioso

Violin

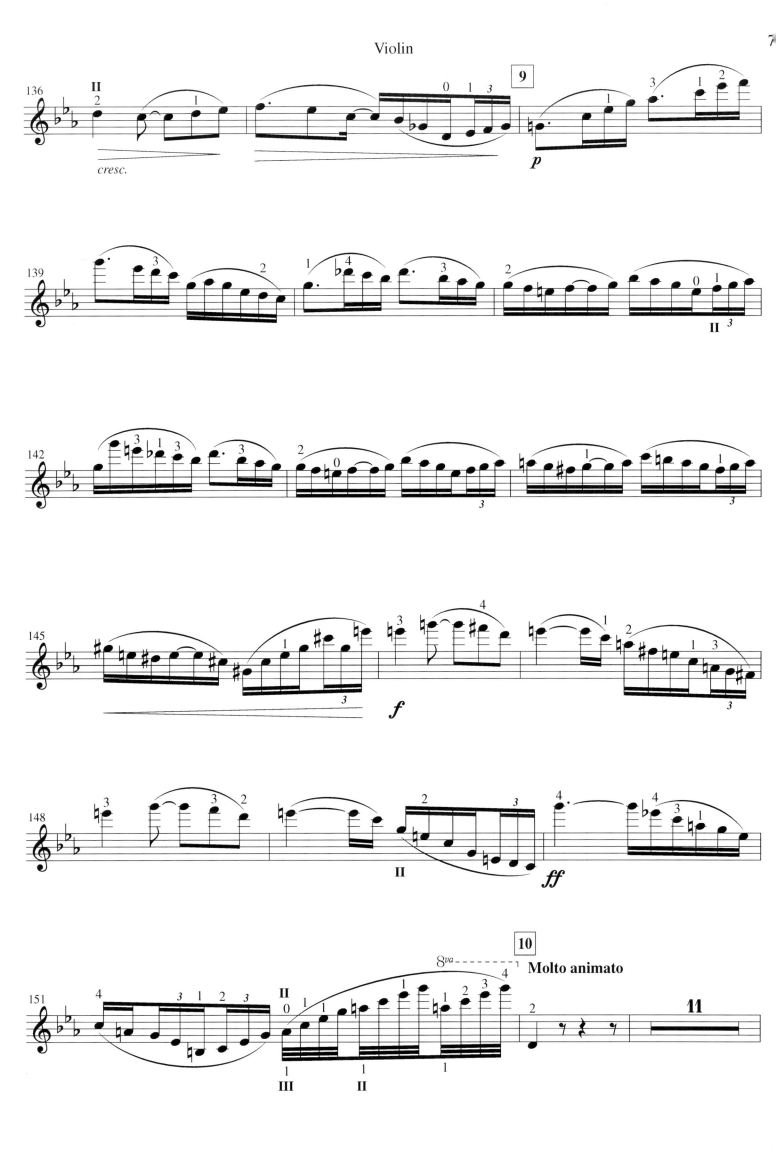

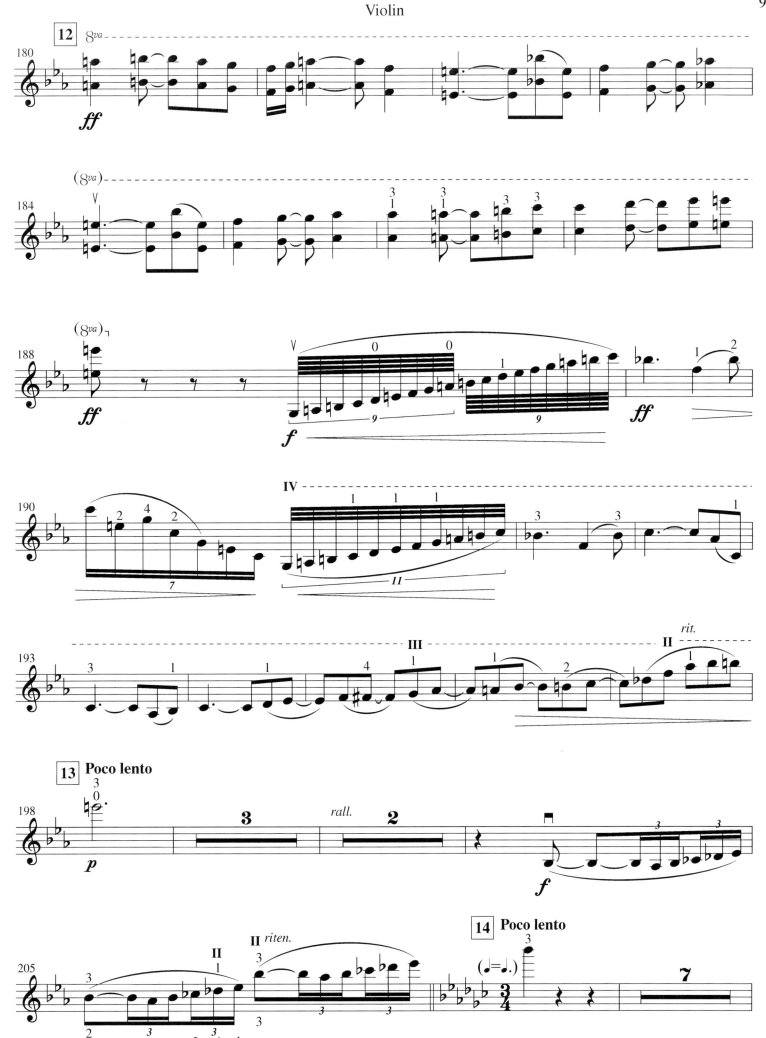

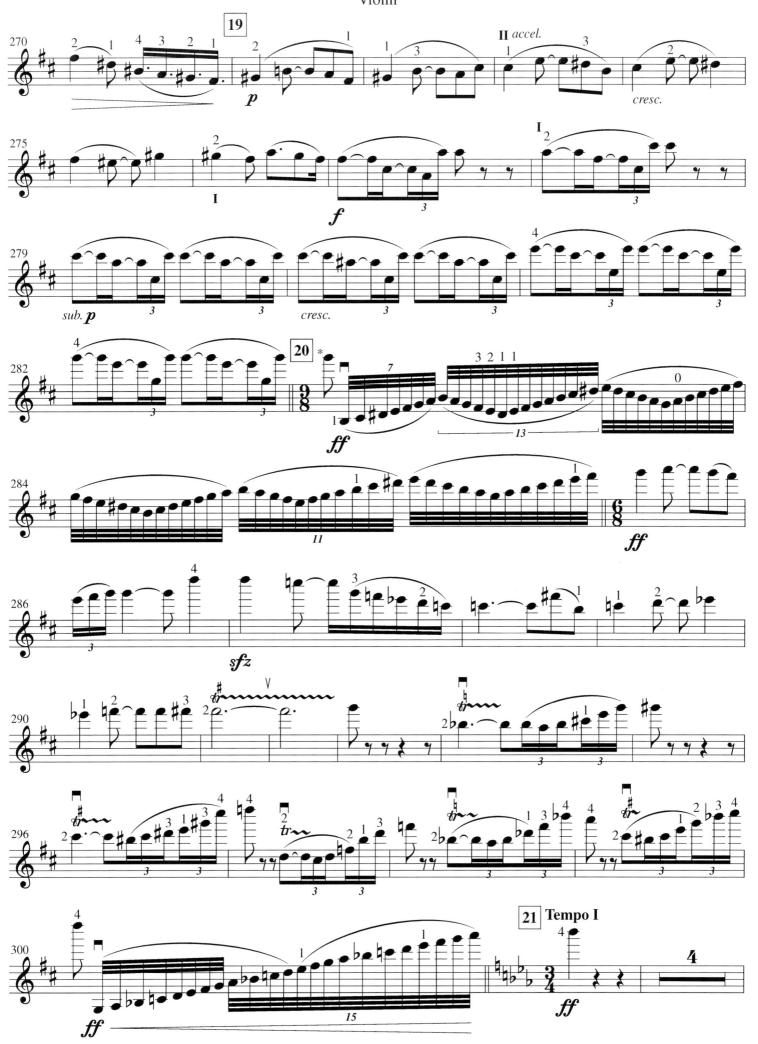

*The downbeat of bar 283 (rehearsal mark: 20) should probably be B instead of G.

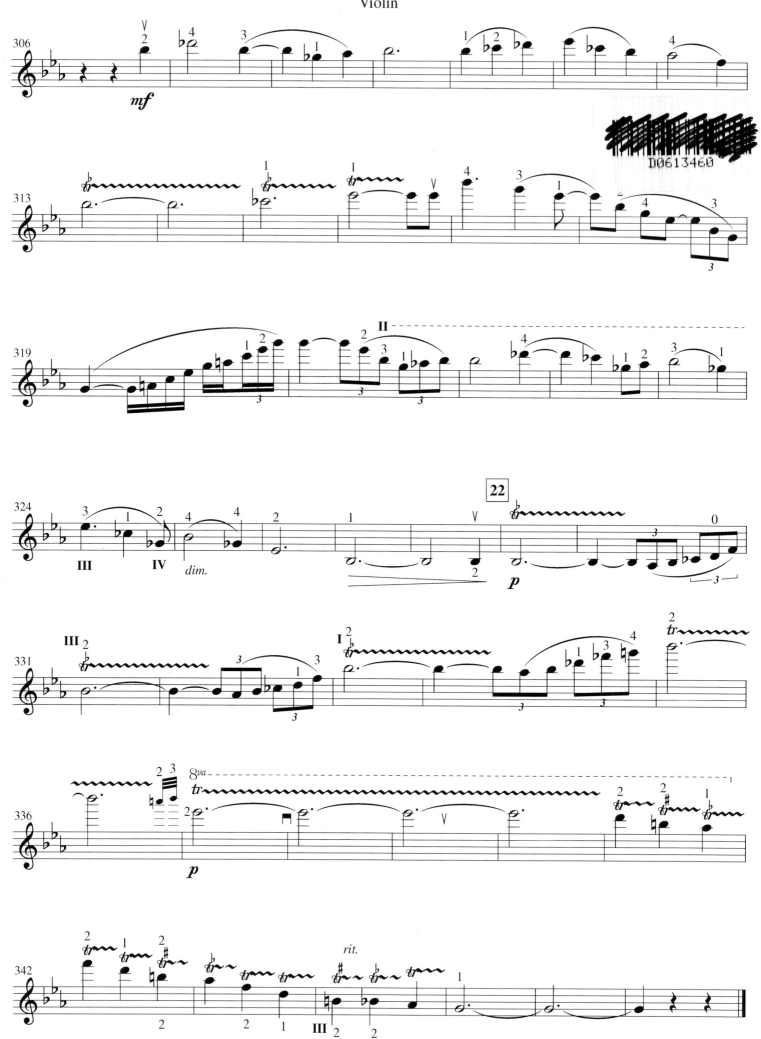